Bones the Sea Dog

CW00863833

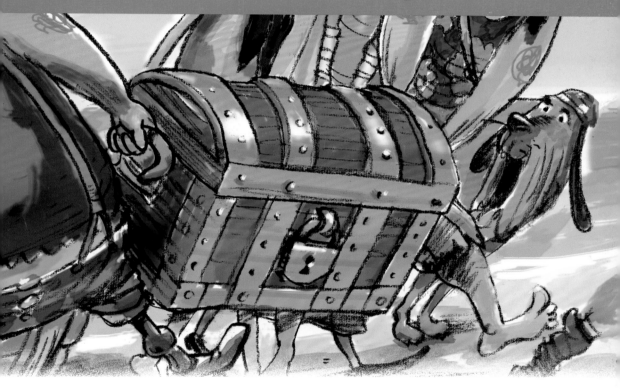

Written by Lisa Thompson
Pictures by Craig Smith and Lew Keilar

HALLAM PRIMARY SCHOOL
HALLAM GRANGE CRESCENT
SHEFFIELD
S10 4BD
TEL (0114) 2304430

Bones had always wanted to be a pirate.

As a puppy, Bones dug holes.

He wasn't looking for bones.

He was looking for treasure.

Bones tied a scarf on his head.

He drew a black patch over his eye.

It made him look like a pirate.

Bones looked for pirate ships out to sea.

One day, Bones spotted a tiny, black dot.

The dot turned into a ship.

The ship was flying a pirate flag.

Bones watched and waited.

The ragged pirates came ashore.

They were carrying a heavy, sea chest.

"Wow! Pirate treasure," said Bones.

The Captain looked for a good spot
to hide the treasure.

"Here is a good spot," said the Captain.
"Hand me the spade."

"Spade?" said one of the pirates.
"You didn't tell us to bring a spade."

"Do I have to tell you everything?"
said the Captain.
"How can we hide the treasure now?"

"Pesky Pirates!" piped up Fingers, the parrot.

Bones ran up. This was just the job for him. In no time at all, he had dug a deep hole.

"Flying cannonballs!" cried the Captain.

"We have found a new pirate for our crew.
Bones, the Sea Dog!" cried the Captain.

The pirates dropped the chest into the hole.
Bones filled up the hole in no time at all.

18

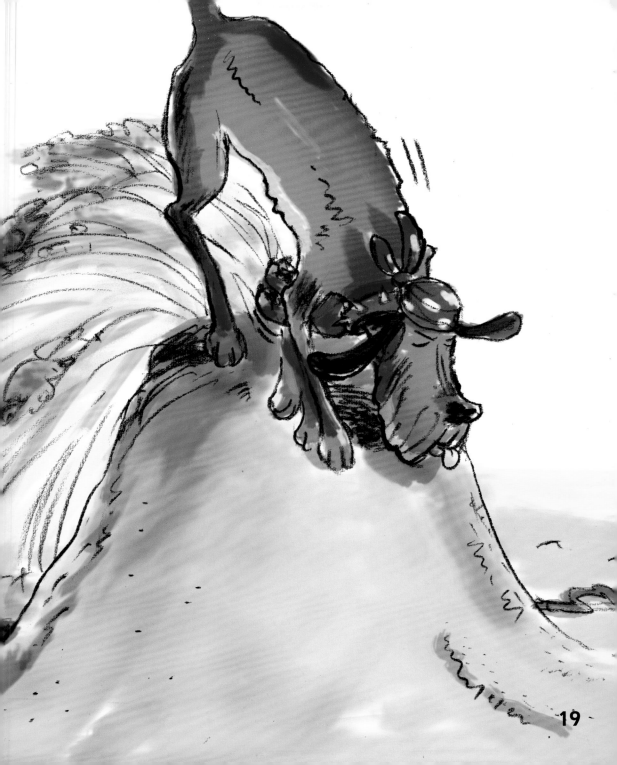

The Captain found just the job for Bones back on the ship.

Bones climbed up to the top of the mast and he looked out for other ships.

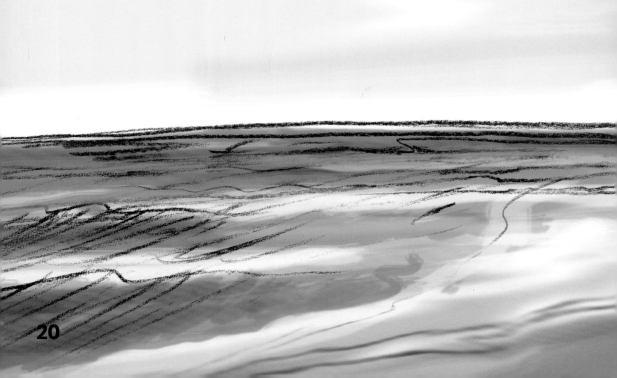

Bones loved his new job.

He could sniff a ship before the rest of the crew could see it.

But best of all, he still loved to dig for treasure.